Literacy BASICS

FOR AGES 9-10 KEY STAGE 2

Contents

Synonyms

Look and learn

Synonyms are words with **similar** meanings.

The knight was very **brave**.
He was **courageous**.

Practice

Underline the pairs of synonyms in each set.

1. brave <u>new</u> wet <u>modern</u>	**2.** wander climb clear roam
3. look assist help run	**4.** blue broad sharp wide
5. start begin break rub	**6.** long cunning sly tall
7. straight feeble low weak	**8.** difficult long blunt hard
9. strong powerful misty tight	**10.** slim thick fast slender
11. blink race sleep run	**12.** stare peer shout snore

Challenge

Join up the synonyms.

cross annoyed
irritated upset

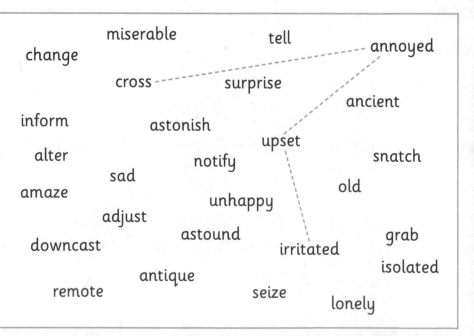

miserable
change   tell   annoyed
                cross ----- surprise
                                        ancient
inform   astonish
alter   notify   upset   snatch
            sad
amaze   unhappy   old
            adjust
downcast   astound   grab
                                    irritated   isolated
        antique
    remote   seize   lonely

2

Direct and reported speech

Look and learn

We can write speech in two ways – as **direct speech** or as **reported speech**.

The old lady said, "My bag is heavy."

The old lady said that her bag was heavy.

This is **direct speech**.
The old lady's exact words are inside the speech marks.

This is **reported speech**.
The old lady's exact words are not used. Speech marks are not used either.

Practice

After each sentence, write if direct speech (DS) or reported speech (RS) is used.

1. "Why are you late?" the teacher asked. (_DS_)
2. The doctor said that the boy had measles. (___)
3. Mr Shah remarked that it was a lovely day. (___)
4. "Please help me wash up, Tom," Mr Simms requested. (___)
5. "Send for the police!" the man shouted. (___)
6. Shireen said that she would come with us. (___)
7. Emma said, "I will come with you." (___)
8. "It's too cold," the lady complained. (___)

Challenge

Write these sentences as reported speech.
1. "How old are you?" the boy asked the old man.
   The boy asked the old man how old he was.
2. "Bring me my dinner," the queen ordered the servant.

3. The teacher said, "You must do your homework, Ben."

4. "It's snowing!" the children cried.

5. "My car can go fast," boasted the racing driver.

3

Common expressions

Look and learn

We use many **common expressions** in our language. Sometimes they are a little hard to understand.

For example, if someone has a crazy idea we say that they have **a bee in their bonnet!**

Practice

Choose the correct word to complete each saying.

canoe	rat	bone	mouth	trumpet
music	fence	water	leaf	bull

1. to have a ___bone___ to pick with someone

2. to take the _____ by the horns

3. to paddle your own _____

4. to sit on the _____

5. to turn over a new _____

6. to face the _____

7. to smell a _____

8. to blow your own _____

9. to get into hot _____

10. to live from hand to _____

Challenge

Match up each common expression with its meaning.

1. to bury the hatchet — to act unfairly

2. to let the cat out of the bag — to do things for yourself

3. to hit below the belt — to make a fresh start

4. to smell a rat — to be a spoilsport

5. to paddle your own canoe — to make peace

6. to blow your own trumpet — to make small difficulties seem bigger

7. to be a wet blanket — to make someone feel unwelcome

8. to make a mountain out of a molehill — to be suspicious

9. to turn over a new leaf — to give away a secret

10. to give someone the cold shoulder — to boast about yourself

Adverbs

Look and learn

An **adverb** tells us **more about a verb**. Many adverbs end with the suffix **ly**.

The burglar opened the window **quietly**.

Practice

Choose the best adverb to complete each sentence.

1. I shouted ____loudly____. (sadly / loudly)

2. The child sang _____. (wisely / sweetly)

3. The girl wrote _____. (neatly / narrowly)

4. The baby chuckled _____. (sadly / contentedly)

5. The teacher explained the sum _____. (clearly / wildly)

6. I whispered _____. (hopefully / quietly)

7. The man asked _____. (politely / painfully)

8. The dog barked _____. (slowly / noisily)

9. The children argued _____. (angrily / wetly)

10. The runner gasped _____. (coldly / breathlessly)

Challenge

1. Write the adverb that can be made from each adjective.

a) clever ____cleverly____   **b)** hopeful _____   **c)** sudden _____

d) cruel _____   **e)** kind _____   **f)** honest _____

g) thankful _____   **h)** grateful _____   **i)** quiet _____

j) patient _____   **k)** safe _____   **l)** careful _____

2. Write the adjective from which each adverb comes.

a) hungrily ____hungry____   **b)** miserably _____   **c)** easily _____

d) nobly _____   **e)** gently _____   **f)** lazily _____

g) busily _____   **h)** wearily _____   **i)** simply _____

j) terribly _____   **k)** nastily _____   **l)** incredibly _____

Plurals

Look and learn

Rule 1. When a word ends in **s**, **x**, **sh** or **ch**, we add **es** to make it plural.

box   box**es**

Rule 2. When a word ends with **f** (or **fe**), we usually change the **f** to **v** and add **es** to make it plural.

loaf   loa**ves**

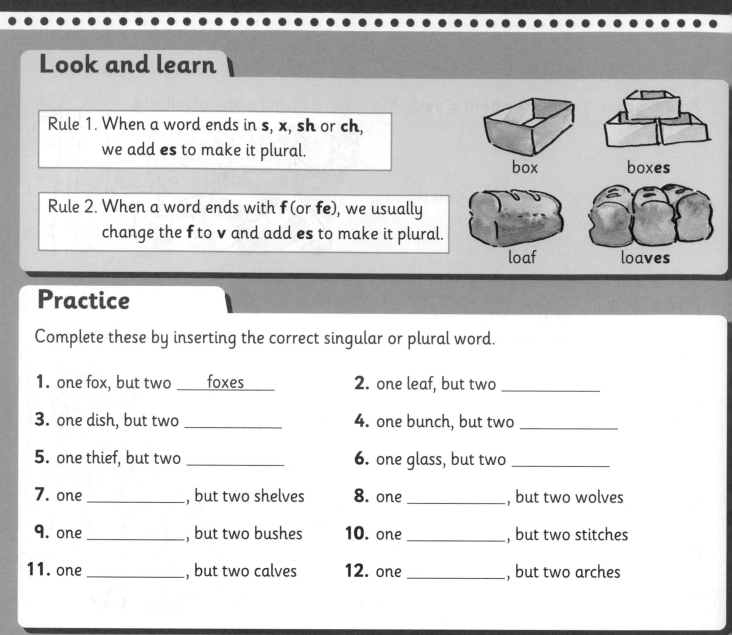

Practice

Complete these by inserting the correct singular or plural word.

1. one fox, but two ___foxes___

2. one leaf, but two _____

3. one dish, but two _____

4. one bunch, but two _____

5. one thief, but two _____

6. one glass, but two _____

7. one _____, but two shelves

8. one _____, but two wolves

9. one _____, but two bushes

10. one _____, but two stitches

11. one _____, but two calves

12. one _____, but two arches

Challenge

Write each sentence again. Change each underlined noun into the plural.

1. The <u>fox</u> hid behind the <u>bush</u>.
   <u>The foxes hid behind the bushes.</u>

2. The baker put the <u>loaf</u> on the <u>shelf</u>.
   _____

3. The <u>thief</u> stole the <u>dish</u>.
   _____

4. I put the <u>knife</u> and the <u>glass</u> on the table.
   _____

5. I painted the <u>leaf</u> with the <u>brush</u>.
   _____

6. The <u>wolf</u> ran off when the <u>bus</u> approached.
   _____

Joining sentences

Look and learn

Two sentences may often be made into one sentence by using a **conjunction**.

The children went indoors. It was raining.

The children went indoors **because** it was raining.

This is a conjunction.

Practice

Think of a suitable conjunction to complete the sentences.

1. The wind was cold ___because___ it was winter.
2. We went for a swim _____ it got too hot.
3. You need not come with us _____ you don't want to.
4. We looked everywhere for the pen _____ could not find it.
5. We are going for a picnic _____ it stays fine.
6. I went to bed _____ I had cleaned my teeth.
7. We watched the squirrel _____ it climbed the tree.
8. We stayed out _____ it got dark.
9. The girl cried _____ she was told off.
10. I whistled _____ I rode my bike.

Challenge

Think of a good ending for each sentence.

1. I will come with you if _____
2. I can't help you unless _____
3. I will make a cup of tea while _____
4. I climbed the mountain although _____
5. The bus stopped when _____
6. I waited until _____
7. I can swim but _____
8. I had a bath because _____

Prefixes

Look and learn

A **prefix** is a group of letters that goes **in front** of a word. Prefixes **change the meanings** of the words.

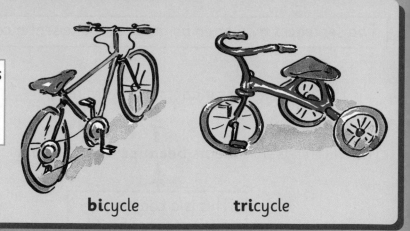

bicycle   **tri**cycle

Practice

The prefixes **il**, **im**, **in** and **ir** often give words the opposite meaning. Say which tense it is in.

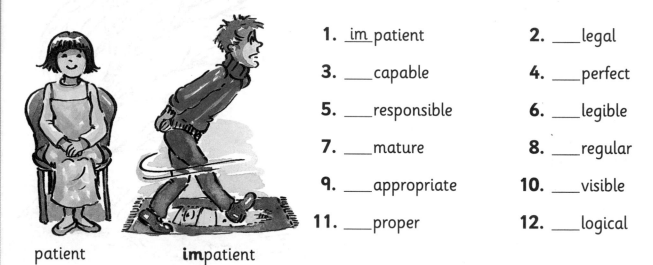

patient   **im**patient

1. _im_ patient
2. ___legal
3. ___capable
4. ___perfect
5. ___responsible
6. ___legible
7. ___mature
8. ___regular
9. ___appropriate
10. ___visible
11. ___proper
12. ___logical

Challenge

Take the prefix off each word. Write the root word you are left with.

1. triangle _____angle_____
2. bimonthly _____
3. transplant _____
4. autograph _____
5. television _____
6. transform _____
7. biplane _____
8. telecommunication _____
9. telescope _____
10. malfunction _____
11. centimetre _____
12. illiterate _____

Auxiliary verbs

Look and learn

Spike **was** washing the car.

Sometimes a verb needs an extra **helper** (or **auxiliary**) verb to help it make sense.

Practice

Choose the correct auxiliary verb to complete each sentence.

1. Emma ____is____ waiting for a bus.   (is / are)
2. I _____ going home soon.   (are / am)
3. We _____ going home soon.   (are / am)
4. What _____ you hear?   (can / does)
5. The cars _____ going too fast.   (was / were)
6. Sophy _____ not get home until midnight.   (am / did)
7. _____ you think that is fair?   (do / shall)
8. I _____ been asleep.   (has / have)
9. Why _____ it rain so much?   (does / do)
10. What _____ the teacher say?   (were / did)

Challenge

Think of a sensible auxiliary verb to complete each sentence.

1. Next week I _____ be ten.
2. _____ you stand on your head?
3. What _____ you like to eat?
4. The girl _____ riding her bike.
5. "_____ you do that?" the man requested.
6. Tomorrow I _____ going on holiday.
7. You _____ not shout in a library.
8. Jenny tried hard but she _____ not keep the secret.

Suffixes

Look and learn

A **suffix** is a group of letters that can be added to the **end** of a word to **change its meaning** or the **way it is used**.

When we enjoy something it gives us enjoyment.

enjoy ➞ enjoy**ment**

It was very dark. Darkness had fallen.

dark ➞ dark**ness**

Practice

Do the suffix word sums.

1. treat + ment = _____treatment_____

2. comfort + able = _____

3. danger + ous = _____

4. critic + al = _____

5. fail + ure = _____

6. differ + ence = _____

7. slow + ly = _____

8. perform + ance = _____

9. just + ice = _____

10. friend + ship = _____

11. king + dom = _____

12. leak + age = _____

Challenge

Write the words in pairs according to their suffixes.

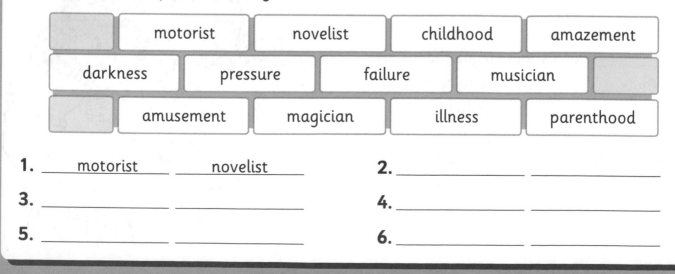

motorist	novelist	childhood	amazement
darkness	pressure	failure	musician
amusement	magician	illness	parenthood

1. ____motorist____ ____novelist____

2. _____ _____

3. _____ _____

4. _____ _____

5. _____ _____

6. _____ _____

Verb tenses

Look and learn

Yesterday I **rode** my bike.

Now I **am walking**.

Tomorrow I **will drive** my car.

| This happened in the **past**. | This is happening **now**. | This will happen in the **future**. |
| The verb is in the **past tense**. | The verb is in the **present tense**. | The verb is in the **future tense**. |

Practice

Underline the verb in each sentence. Say which tense it is in .

1. Last week I <u>swam</u> in the sea.
2. In years to come we will land on Mars.
3. I am writing a book.
4. The sun is shining.
5. Next week we will go on holiday.
6. In 1066 the Normans invaded Britain.
7. Tom shouted at his sister.
8. Mr Shah is sitting on the bench.
9. Will it rain this afternoon?
10. Who is knocking at the door?

	past	present	future
1.	✓		
2.			
3.			
4.			
5.			
6.			
7.			
8.			
9.			
10.			

Challenge

Complete this chart.

	present tense	past tense	future tense
1.	I talk	I talked	I will talk
2.	you shout		
3.	he washes		
4.	she likes		
5.	it vanishes		
6.	we look		
7.	you knock		
8.	they call		

Syllables

Look and learn

We can break words down into **smaller units of sound**, called **syllables**.
Notice how words with a **double consonant** in them are split up.

pup – pet

lug – gage

Practice

Join up these to make sensible words.

1. pup	gage	_____
2. bag	fic	_____
3. rab	py	_____puppy_____
4. stop	ter	_____
5. traf	ply	_____
6. fol	bit	_____
7. sup	my	_____
8. fun	per	_____
9. clam	nel	_____
10. but	low	_____

Challenge

Split these words into syllables.

1. rubbish rub–bish_____   **2.** button _____

3. attend _____   **4.** adder _____

5. pillow _____   **6.** cutting _____

7. happen _____   **8.** horrid _____

9. willow _____   **10.** pepper _____

11. robber _____   **12.** affect _____

Common letter strings

Look and learn

Some words with the same **letter strings** are **pronounced differently**.

gu**i**de   fr**ui**t

Practice

The words in each set have the same letter strings but are pronounced differently.
Underline the odd one out in each set.

1. but   cut   <u>put</u>
2. enough   through   tough
3. crow   now   flow
4. one   bone   cone
5. foot   boot   root
6. love   glove   move
7. height   eight   weight
8. match   watch   catch
9. moth   broth   both
10. dull   pull   gull

Challenge

| plough | through | although | bought | enough |
| drought | tough | bough | cough | thought |

Write the word or words that rhyme with:

1. off   <u>cough</u>
2. cow   _____
3. snow   _____
4. stuff   _____
5. court   _____
6. new   _____
7. out   _____

Subject/verb agreement

Look and learn

The **subject** and the **verb** in each sentence must agree with each other.

A dog **was** barking.

Some dogs **were** barking.

Practice

Choose the correct form of the verb to agree with the subject in each sentence.

1. Ali ___likes___ curry.   (like / likes)

2. The bike _____ a new tyre.   (need / needs)

3. The boy _____ late for school.   (is / are)

4. Squirrels _____ trees.   (climb / climbs)

5. The children _____ naughty.   (was / were)

6. Who _____ it?   (did / done)

7. The boy _____ measles.   (has / have)

8. The dogs _____ fierce.   (is / are)

9. Robots _____ in a strange way.   (talk / talks)

10. The bird _____ loudly.   (sing / sings)

Challenge

Write each sentence correctly.

1. We was late for school.   We were late for school. _____

2. He done it yesterday. _____

3. Snails crawls on walls. _____

4. I wants a sweet. _____

5. She were shopping. _____

6. He don't care any more. _____

7. The apples is rotten. _____

8. Sam have lots of homework. _____

Onomatopoeia

Look and learn

Onomatopoeia is when the **sound** of the word is **similar** to the **sound of the thing it describes**.

WOOF! WOOF!

CLANG!

Practice

Match up each animal with the sound it makes.

1. dog
2. cat
3. cow
4. duck
5. sheep
6. snake
7. horse
8. turkey
9. bee
10. mouse

Quack!

Woof!

Hiss!

Baa!

Gobble!

Miaow!

Neigh!

Buzz!

Squeak!

Moo!

Challenge

Think of something that:

1. screeches _____

2. gurgles _____

3. crunches _____

4. rattles _____

5. sizzles _____

6. ticks _____

7. thunders _____

8. wails _____

9. pops _____

10. blares _____

11. jingles _____

12. twangs _____

Homophones

Look and learn

Homophones are words that **sound the same**, but are **spelled differently**.

We are not **allowed** to talk **aloud** in the library.

Practice

Choose the correct homophone to complete each sentence.

1. The __plane__ took off from the airport. (plain / plane)
2. Avoid _____ whenever possible. (waste / waist)
3. I had another _____ of cake. (peace / piece)
4. I love _____ buns. (currant / current)
5. Do you _____ apples? (peal / peel)
6. We took the quickest _____. (root / route)
7. There is a good _____ on TV. (cereal / serial)
8. Some people _____ every day. (pray / prey)
9. The burglar had nerves of _____. (steal / steel)
10. Our boat needed a new _____. (sale / sail)

Challenge

Think of a homophone to match each of these.

1. ball __bawl__   2. board _____   3. dear _____

4. flower _____   5. grown _____   6. hair _____

7. key _____   8. not _____   9. made _____

10. medal _____   11. pain _____   12. raise _____

Soft c and g

Look and learn

a **g**entle **g**iant

When the letter **g** is followed by **e**, **i** or **y**, it makes a **j** sound.

a ni**c**e **c**ity

When the letter **c** is followed by **e**, **i** or **y**, it makes an **s** sound.

Practice

Write the word from the box to match the meaning. Underline the soft **c** or **g** in each word.

1. the opposite of princess   prin<u>c</u>e _____
2. the middle   _____
3. a reddish-brown colour   _____
4. allows a door to open   _____
5. a hundred years   _____
6. unusual   _____
7. the opposite of 'mean'   _____
8. a room in a prison   _____
9. used for separating pieces of land   _____
10. hair that hangs over the forehead   _____
11. to move to music   _____
12. someone who is very intelligent   _____

generous
ginger
genius
fringe
hinge
strange
centre
century
cell
dance
fence
prince

Challenge

Choose **ice**, **ace** or **age** to complete each word.

1. vill<u>age</u>

2. pol_____

3. f_____

4. gr_____

5. off_____

6. sav_____

7. post_____

8. tw_____

9. br_____

10. d_____

11. pl_____

12. im_____

17

Antonyms

Look and learn

An **antonym** is a word which has the **opposite** meaning. Sometimes it can be made by adding a **prefix**.

legible   illegible

Practice

Match up the opposites.

1. absent	release
2. capture	destroy
3. coward	present
4. create	friend
5. enemy	hero

6. plentiful	true
7. humble	exit
8. foolish	scarce
9. false	wise
10. entrance	proud

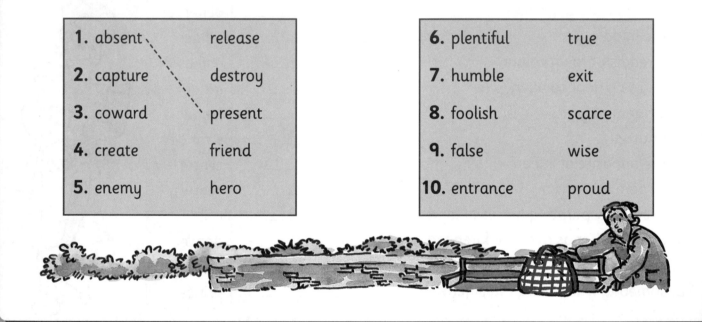

Challenge

1. Choose **un**, **in** or **dis** to make each word mean the opposite.

a) _dis_ appear

b) _____ sane

c) _____ willing

d) _____ welcome

e) _____ agree

f) _____ expensive

g) _____ continue

h) _____ complete

i) _____ conscious

2. For each word write an antonym of five letters.

a) clean _____

b) lost _____

c) late _____

d) asleep _____

e) noisy _____

f) long _____

g) back _____

clean   –   dirty

Doubling the consonant

Look and learn

hop ➞ hopping ➞ hopped

Verbs ending with a **single consonant** preceded by a **short vowel** **double the consonant** before adding the suffix **ing** or **ed**.

Practice

Complete this chart.

	root verb	+ suffix **ing**	+ suffix **ed**
1.	stop	stopping	stopped
2.	wag		wagged
3.		nodding	
4.			ripped
5.	jog		
6.			tapped
7.		tugging	
8.	bat		
9.			rubbed
10.	hum		
11.		sagging	
12.			banned

Challenge

Correct the spelling of the verb in each sentence that is wrong.

1. Sally was taping her foot to the music. _____tapping_____
2. The teacher pined up some pictures. _____
3. The mugger robed the old lady. _____
4. I hoped on one leg. _____
5. The balloon poped with a bang. _____
6. The dog was waging its tail. _____
7. I like wining races. _____
8. I riped my trousers on the barbed wire. _____

Make it clear

Look and learn

The elephant raised its **trunk**.

Sometimes the meanings of words or sentences can be **ambiguous** (unclear).

Practice

Tick the meanings of the underlined word in each sentence.

1. The <u>coach</u> helped me improve my football.   a small bus ☐   a sports trainer ☑
2. I ate a <u>date</u>.   a type of fruit ☐   a specific time ☐
3. I grew potatoes on my <u>plot</u>.   a plan ☐   a piece of land ☐
4. I drew a line with the <u>ruler</u>.   a measuring device ☐   a royal person ☐
5. The <u>wave</u> knocked me over.   the motion of the sea ☐   a greeting ☐
6. I can <u>stamp</u> my foot.   you stick it on a letter ☐   put your foot down hard ☐
7. The <u>match</u> was cancelled.   the game ☐   used for lighting a fire ☐
8. The <u>bank</u> was muddy.   where money is kept ☐   the side of a river ☐
9. I ate the <u>mint</u>.   where money is made ☐   a type of sweet ☐
10. The soldier drove the <u>tank</u>.   an armoured vehicle ☐   a water container ☐

Challenge

In your own words, make the meaning of each of these clearer.

1. I feel like a cup of tea.   <u>I would like a cup of tea.</u>
2. I told the chef I cooked myself.   _____
3. Keep medicines safe. If there are children in the house lock them up.   _____
4. LOST. Dog belonging to lady with long fur.   _____
5. The policeman found the lorry full of sheep that had run out of fuel.   _____

Standard English

Look and learn

Standard English is the kind of language used in education, government and business.

Me and Lee played football.

Lee and I played football.

This is not grammatically correct.

This is how it is written in Standard English.

Practice

Match up each non-standard sentence with the correct Standard English sentence.

1. We done it last week.
2. Me and Sam went home.
3. It were funny.
4. The sweets wasn't on the shelf.
5. I ain't got no crisps.
6. He don't come no more.
7. I wanna go.
8. Where yer going?
9. Tom ain't in.
10. We going soon.

It was funny.
I have not got any crisps.
Where are you going?
We did it last week.
He does not come any more.
Tom is not in.
We are going soon.
Sam and I went home.
I want to go.
The sweets were not on the shelf.

Challenge

Write these sentences in Standard English.

1. Whose got me book?   <u>Who has got my book?</u>
2. He didn't do nothing.
3. I don't want no trouble.
4. Here's the story what I wrote.
5. They coming tomorrow.
6. We was just looking.
7. I ain't going nowhere.
8. That's real bad.

Unstressed vowels

Look and learn

When we say some words it is **hard to hear** some of the **vowels**.
These are called **unstressed vowels**.

Veg**e**tables.

Practice

Fill in the missing unstressed vowel in each of the words. Use a dictionary to help you.

1. choc_o_late
2. int__rest
3. diff__rent
4. fact__ry
5. bus__ness
6. temp__rature
7. di__mond
8. myst__ry
9. hist__ry
10. sep__rate
11. t__rrific
12. bre__kfast

Challenge

In each word below an unstressed vowel has been missed out. Write each word correctly.

1. camra _____camera_____
2. valuble _____
3. poisnous _____
4. compny _____
5. captin _____
6. gardner _____
7. cemetry _____
8. evry _____
9. librry _____
10. mathmatics _____

Suffixing verbs ending with e

Look and learn

skate – skating – skated

Yesterday I skated on roller skates.

Now I'm skating on ice.

> When a verb ends with a **magic e**, we usually drop the **e** before we add **ing** or **ed**.

Practice

Complete this chart.

	root verb	+ ing	+ ed
1.	hope	hoping	hoped
2.	use		
3.		dining	
4.			loved
5.		hating	
6.	refuse		
7.	excite		
8.			decided
9.		deserving	
10.	bake		

Challenge

Correct the verbs that are incorrectly spelled in these sentences.

1. I am using a new pen. Yesterday I usd an old one. _____used_____

2. I love baking. I bakt these cakes. _____

3. We decidid to stay in when it rained. _____

4. My dog likes chaseing cats. _____

5. It was an exciteing adventure. _____

6. I am hopeing it will snow soon. _____

7. We dind in the dining room. _____

8. We movd house when I changd jobs. _____ _____

Double negatives

Look and learn

The dog hasn't got no whiskers. ☒

This sentence contains a **double negative**.

The dog hasn't got any whiskers. ☑

This sentence is **correctly** written.

Practice

Match up each incorrect sentence with its correct version.

1. There isn't no point in cheating.
2. I don't want no arguments.
3. The man wasn't nowhere to be seen.
4. I don't belong to no club.
5. We didn't see no one.
6. I haven't never been abroad.
7. I never went nowhere yesterday.
8. The boy didn't say nothing.
9. I haven't got no money.
10. I never did nothing wrong.

I don't want any arguments.

We didn't see anyone.

I didn't go anywhere yesterday.

I haven't got any money.

There isn't any point in cheating.

The boy didn't say anything.

I don't belong to any club.

I didn't do anything wrong.

The man wasn't anywhere to be seen.

I haven't ever been abroad.

Challenge

Write each sentence correctly.

1. The car hadn't got no engine.   The car did not have an engine.
2. I never got no sums right.   _____
3. She don't come home no more.   _____
4. I haven't never seen the Queen.   _____
5. She didn't go nowhere near him.   _____
6. I'm not never going there again.   _____
7. I don't want no help.   _____
8. She didn't know nothing.   _____

Sentences and phrases

Look and learn

The driver parked his lorry in the street.

in the street

| A **sentence** contains a **verb**. It **makes sense** on its own. | A **phrase** does **not contain a verb**. It does **not make sense on its own**. |

Practice

Write if each of the following is a sentence (S) or a phrase (P).

1. The girls played netball.   (_S_)

2. in the park   (__)

3. this morning   (__)

4. The sun came out.   (__)

5. Tom went swimming.   (__)

6. after lunch   (__)

7. The lightning flashed in the sky.   (__)

8. greenish-brown   (__)

9. through the town   (__)

10. I had eggs for dinner.   (__)

Challenge

Make up six sentences. Include one of these phrases in each.

| because of the rain | that night | through the tunnel |
| outside the house | huge and hairy | down the hill |

1. _____

2. _____

3. _____

4. _____

5. _____

6. _____

Clauses

Look and learn

A **clause** is a **group of words** which can be used as a **whole sentence** or as **part of a sentence**. A clause must contain a **verb** and have a **subject**.

Edward fought a scary dragon.

↑ subject ↑ verb

This is a one-clause sentence.

Practice

Underline the subject and circle the verb in each one-clause sentence.

1. Emma (ate) a huge ice cream.
2. The children bought a ticket at the station.
3. The lady looked around the museum.
4. Mark scored the winning goal.
5. Helicopters fly in the sky.
6. Some girls ride bikes.
7. The huge monster roared loudly.
8. Out of the cave came the bear.
9. During the night the wind howled.
10. We found an old chest in the attic.

Challenge

Think of a suitable subject for each of these one-clause sentences.

1. _____ landed the plane safely.
2. _____ chased the boy across the field.
3. _____ growled fiercely.
4. _____ skidded off the road.
5. _____ walked in space.
6. _____ cut the lady's hair.
7. _____ looked down my throat.
8. _____ hooted in the woods.
9. _____ ploughed the field with a tractor.
10. _____ blew the whistle at the football match.

Prepositions

Look and learn

A **preposition** tells us the **position of** one thing in relation to another.

Sam hid **behind** the tree.

Practice

Choose a suitable preposition to complete each sentence.

1. You cross ___over___ a bridge.
2. You sit _____ a chair.
3. You swim _____ the sea.
4. You get _____ of a car.
5. You climb _____ a ladder.
6. You fall _____ a wall.
7. You go _____ a tunnel.
8. You fall _____ a hole.
9. You jump _____ a narrow stream.
10. You hide _____ the door.

in		
		down
up		
		on
over		
		out
off		
		over
behind		
		through

Challenge

Which prepositions usually go with these words?

1. according ___to___	2. interfere _____	3. guilty _____
4. comment _____	5. similar _____	6. satisfied _____
7. inspired _____	8. shrink _____	9. acquainted _____
10. rely _____	11. victim _____	12. plunge _____
13. mix _____	14. opposite _____	15. agree _____

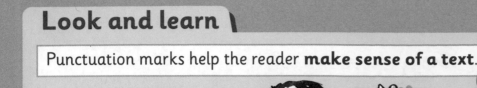

Look and learn

Punctuation marks help the reader **make sense of a text**.

Mrs Shah exclaimed what a lovely present.

This is hard to read.

Mrs Shah exclaimed, "What a lovely present!"

This is easier to read.

Practice

In the sentences below, all the commas have been missed out. Put them in.

1. "My dog is called Smudge" Joe said.
2. I ate an apple a banana a pear and some grapes.
3. The car an old banger came to a halt.
4. After what seemed an age the pop singer appeared.
5. The child muttered " I hate cabbage!"
6. "Pass me the salt Tom" Mrs Jones said.
7. My favourite colours are red blue yellow and green.
8. "Good morning Mrs Smith" I said.
9. Mount Everest tall and snow-covered towered above us.
10. Pam who looked rather frightened bolted out of the door.

Challenge

Write each sentence and punctuate it correctly.
1. Would you like to go shopping Mrs Smith asked

_____

2. the baker said sam put the loaves on the shelves please

_____

3. mr barnes shouted my house is on fire

_____

4. im fed up samir said what can I do

_____

5. mrs collins who was getting angry shouted loudly

_____

Apostrophes for possession

Look and learn

We use **apostrophes** to show who or what something **belongs to**.

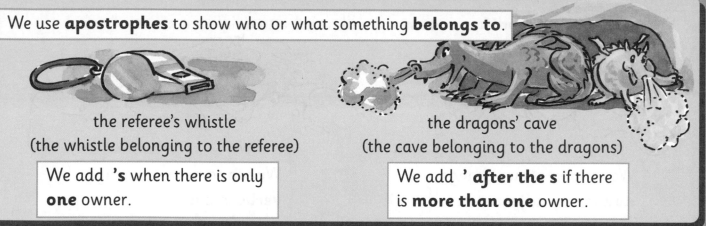

the referee's whistle
(the whistle belonging to the referee)

the dragons' cave
(the cave belonging to the dragons)

We add **'s** when there is only **one** owner.

We add **'** **after the s** if there is **more than one** owner.

Practice

Rewrite each phrase using an apostrophe.

1. the pencil belonging to the boy   the boy's pencil
2. the car belonging to the teacher _____
3. the bone belonging to the dog _____
4. the bike belonging to Tom _____
5. the ring belonging to the king _____
6. the bag belonging to Mrs Patel _____
7. the helmet belonging to the policeman _____
8. the ladder belonging to Mr Brent _____
9. the tail belonging to the cat _____
10. the banana belonging to the gorilla _____

Challenge

Write these out in full.

1. the bird's eggs   the eggs belonging to the bird
2. the dancer's shoes _____
3. the horses' hooves _____
4. the lady's hat _____
5. the baker's shop _____
6. the boys' bicycles _____
7. the girl's shorts _____
8. the squirrel's tail _____
9. the crocodiles' teeth _____
10. the teacher's books _____

Making new words

Look and learn

We can sometimes **modify** a **root word** and turn it into a different **class of word**.

beauty ⟶ beautiful

We can sometimes change **nouns** into **adjectives**.

invent ⟶ invention

We can sometimes change **verbs** into **nouns**.

Practice

Match up the correct adjective with the noun it comes from.

	Nouns	Adjectives		Nouns	Adjectives
1.	accident	athletic	7.	expense	fashionable
2.	affection	childish	8.	faith	woollen
3.	athlete	accidental	9.	fashion	faithful
4.	caution	cowardly	10.	favour	furry
5.	child	cautious	11.	fur	favourite
6.	coward	affectionate	12.	wool	expensive

Challenge

Work out the verb from which each noun is made.

1. movement _move_

2. assistance _____

3. departure _____

4. discovery _____

5. behaviour _____

6. adoption _____

7. communication _____

8. beginning _____

9. injury _____

10. recognition _____

11. service _____

12. thought _____

Connecting clauses together

Look and learn

We sometimes use a **connecting word** (or words) to **join** two clauses together.

I like the weekends **because** I can stay up late.

Practice

Choose the best ending for each sentence. Underline the connecting words.

1. Emma is good at Maths
2. I like to wear a monster mask
3. I am wearing boots
4. I got excited
5. We had to run to the shops
6. We fly our kites
7. I had a drink
8. John kept reading
9. I ate some cabbage
10. We saw a man

because I am going to play football.
whenever it is windy.
until it was time for bed.
<u>but</u> she is hopeless at spelling.
who was very tall.
before they closed.
although I didn't like it.
so I can frighten people.
after I had eaten my sandwich.
when my favourite singer came on TV.

Challenge

Think of a clause to complete each of these.
1. The stars twinkled as _____
2. I climbed the ladder so that _____
3. I had to run fast because _____
4. We found an old chest that _____
5. Your book is exciting but _____
6. The tree swayed when _____
7. I did not recognise the thief until _____
8. I get anxious whenever _____
9. I had to have a bath because _____
10. Tim kept shouting even though _____

Answers

● ●

Page 2
Practice: 2. wander/roam, 3. assist/help,
4. broad/wide, 5. start/begin, 6. cunning/sly,
7. feeble/weak, 8. difficult/hard,
9. strong/powerful, 10. slim/slender,
11. race/run, 12. stare/peer
Challenge:
change, alter, adjust
inform, notify, tell
amaze, astound, astonish, surprise
downcast, miserable, sad, unhappy
remote, isolated, lonely
antique, old, ancient
grab, snatch, seize

Page 3
Practice: 2. (RS), 3. (RS), 4. (DS),
5. (DS), 6. (RS), 7. (DS), 8. (DS)
Challenge:
  2. The queen ordered the servant to bring
     her dinner.
  3. The teacher told Ben to do his
     homework.
  4. The children cried that it was snowing.
  5. The racing driver boasted that his
     car could go fast.

Page 4
Practice: 2. bull, 3. canoe, 4. fence, 5. leaf,
6. music, 7. rat, 8. trumpet, 9. water,
10. mouth
Challenge:
  2. to give away a secret
  3. to act unfairly
  4. to be suspicious
  5. to do things for yourself
  6. to boast about yourself
  7. to be a spoilsport
  8. to make small difficulties seem bigger
  9. to make a fresh start
  10. to make someone feel unwelcome

Page 5
Practice: 2. sweetly, 3. neatly,
4. contentedly, 5. clearly, 6. quietly, 7.
politely, 8. noisily, 9. angrily, 10. breathlessly
Challenge: 1. b) hopefully, c) suddenly,
d) cruelly, e) kindly, f) honestly, g) thankfully,
h) gratefully, i) quietly, j) patiently,
k) safely, l) carefully
2. b) miserable, c) easy, d) noble, e) gentle,
f) lazy, g) busy, h) weary, i) simple, j) terrible,
k) nasty, l) incredible

Page 6
Practice: 2. leaves, 3. dishes, 4. bunches,
5. thieves, 6. glasses, 7. shelf, 8. wolf, 9. bush,
10. stitch, 11. calf, 12. arch
Challenge:
  2. The baker put the loaves on the shelves.
  3. The thieves stole the dishes.
  4. I put the knives and the glasses on the
     table.
  5. I painted the leaves with the brushes.
  6. The wolves ran off when the buses
     approached.

Page 7
Practice: answers may vary
Challenge: answers may vary

Page 8
Practice: 2. illegal, 3. incapable, 4. imperfect,
5. irresponsible, 6. illegible, 7. immature,
8. irregular, 9. inappropriate, 10. invisible,
11. improper, 12. illogical
Challenge: 2. monthly, 3. plant, 4. graph,
5. vision, 6. form, 7. plane, 8. communication,
9. scope, 10. function, 11. metre, 12. literate

Page 9
Practice: 2. am, 3. are, 4. can, 5. were,
6. did, 7. Do, 8. have, 9. does, 10. did
Challenge: answers may vary

Page 10
Practice: 2. comfortable, 3. dangerous,
4. critical, 5. failure, 6. difference, 7. slowly,
8. performance, 9. justice,
10. friendship, 11. kingdom, 12. leakage
Challenge: 2. childhood/parenthood,
3. amazement/amusement,
4. darkness/illness, 5. pressure/failure,
6. musician/magician

Page 11
Practice: 2. will land (future), 3. am writing
(present), 4. is shining (present), 5. will go
(future), 6. invaded (past), 7. shouted (past),
8. is sitting (present), 9. Will rain (future),
10. is knocking (present)
Challenge: 2. you shouted, you will shout,
3. he washed, he will wash, 4. she liked, she
will like, 5. it vanished, it will vanish, 6. we
looked, we will look, 7. you knocked, you will
knock, 8. they called, they will call

Page 12
Practice: 2. baggage, 3.rabbit, 4. stopper,
5. traffic, 6. follow, 7. supply, 8. funnel,
9. clammy, 10. butter
Challenge: 2. but—ton, 3. at—tend,
4. ad—der, 5. pil—low, 6. cut—ting,
7. hap—pen, 8. hor—rid, 9. wil—low,
10. pep—per, 11. rob—ber, 12. af—fect

Page 13
Practice: 2. through, 3. now, 4. one, 5. foot,
6. move, 7. height, 8. watch, 9. both, 10. pull
Challenge: 2. plough, bough, 3. although,
4. tough, enough, 5. thought, bought
6. through, 7. drought

Page 14
Practice: 2. needs, 3. is, 4. climb, 5. were,
6. did, 7. has, 8. are, 9. talk, 10. sings
Challenge:
  2. He did it yesterday.
  3. Snails crawl on walls.
  4. I want a sweet.
  5. She was shopping.
  6. He doesn't care any more.
  7. The apples are rotten.
  8. Sam has lots of homework.

Page 15
Practice: 1. Woof!, 2. Miaow!, 3. Moo!,
4. Quack!, 5. Baa!, 6. Hiss!, 7. Neigh!,
8. Gobble!, 9. Buzz!, 10. Squeak!
Challenge: answers may vary

Page 16
Practice: 2. waste, 3. piece, 4. currant,
5. peel, 6. route, 7. serial, 8. pray, 9. steel,
10. sail
Challenge: answers may vary

Page 17
Practice: 2. centre, 3. ginger, 4. hinge,
5. century, 6. strange, 7. generous, 8. cell,
9. fence, 10. fringe, 11. dance, 12. genius
Challenge: 2. police, 3. face, 4. grace,
5. office, 6. savage, 7. postage, 8. twice,
9. brace, 10. dice, 11. place, 12. image

Page 18
Practice: 2. capture/release, 3. coward/hero,
4. create/destroy, 5. enemy/friend,
6. plentiful/scarce, 7. humble/proud,
8. foolish/wise, 9. false/true, 10. entrance/exit
Challenge: 1. b) insane, c) unwilling,
d) unwelcome, e) disagree, f) inexpensive,
g) discontinue, h) incomplete, i) unconscious
2. a) dirty, b) found, c) early, d) awake,
e) quiet, f) short, g) front

Page 19
Practice: 2. wagging, 3. nod/nodded,
4. rip/ripping, 5. jogging/jogged,
6. tap/tapping, 7. tug/tugged,
8. batting/batted, 9. rub/rubbing,
10. humming/hummed, 11. sag/sagged,
12. ban/banning
Challenge: 2. pinned, 3. robbed, 4. hopped,
5. popped, 6. wagging, 7. winning, 8. ripped